The Famous H

by **KATE GAYNOR**

Illustrated by **RUTH KEATING**

Published in 2008 by

SPECIAL STORIES PUBLISHING

ISBN 978-0-9555787-5-5

A catalogue record for this book is available from the British Library

Special Stories Publishing

www.specialstories.net

Acknowledgements

Many thanks to Kieran, my father Michael, my brother George and my extended family and friends. Special thanks too to my uncle Liam Gaynor, Liz O'Donoghue, Eva Byrne and the Louth County Enterprise Board for their endless encouragement, support and invaluable advice.

Very special thanks to Antoinette Walker B.A., M.A., R.G.N. and Joan Kelly Nursing Services Manager for the Irish Cancer Society.

Special thanks also to Dr. Gerard Molloy Ph.D C.Psychol. whose time and effort with this project was so greatly appreciated.

About the Illustrator

Originally from Kilkenny, Ruth Keating moved to Dublin in 2003. She has recently graduated with a B.A. in Model making and Design for Film and Production Design in I.A.D.T., The National Film School. Ruth likes to travel as much as she can and in her spare time she enjoys sculpture, fashion, reading, music festivals and concerts.

To read more about the special stories collection, visit the Special Stories website at:

www.specialstories.net

for my mum

Hi! my name is **Harry**. I am five years old.

Even though I am the very same as every other boy and girl, there
are some very special things I have to do that other boys and girls
don't.

One of these things is going to visit the hospital and the doctor a lot. My doctor is called Doctor John.

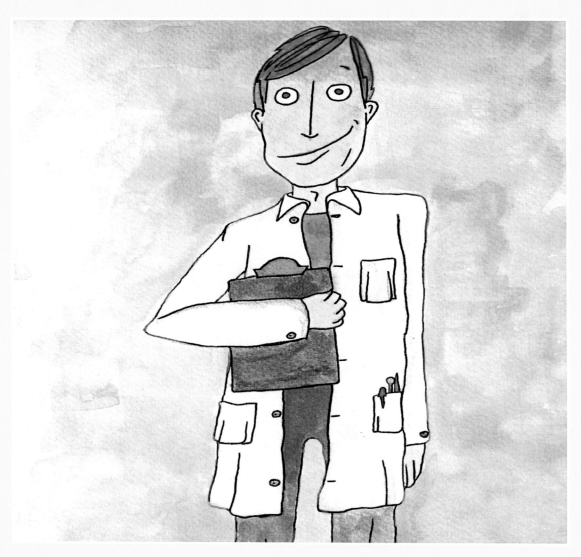

He sometimes wears a white coat and always has a happy kind face. Doctor John always knows what to do when I don't feel very well.

One day when I went to visit him, he said that I was going to have to stay in hospital for a while. I needed to have some medicine put into my body to make me feel much better.

First, I had to have a special tube put into my chest where the medicine would go in. And afterwards I stayed in the rainbow coloured hospital ward to get my medicine. After a few days, I was allowed to go home again.

When you go into hospital you might feel afraid at first. But it won't be long until you make friends with all of the other boys and girls who are in the hospital to get medicine, just like you.

After a few visits to the hospital to get my medicine, I noticed something strange starting to happen. The hair on my head started to come out! And in only a couple of weeks I had no hair left on my head at all.

I was a little afraid when I looked in the mirror and saw my head with no hair on top. But my mum and Doctor John promised that it would come back again soon. In the meantime they told me that someone very special was coming to visit me in the hospital.

The very next day, all the children gathered in the big hospital playroom. Some children were in wheelchairs, some were on beds and others were sitting on big cushions.

I was wearing a special woolly hat that my mum and dad had given me to cover my head because it was a cold head with no hair on it! Then, a BIG surprise! Into the room walked a real-life fireman wearing his yellow fireman's hat!

All the children were so excited! We had never seen a real fireman before. I pulled on the fireman's sleeve, and asked him if I could try on his special fireman's hat.

"Well," he said with a smile, "I'm afraid that fireman's hats are only for firemen. They only fit very special types of heads." "I think that my head is pretty special" I said and pulled off my woolly hat to show the fireman my new head with no hair on top.

13

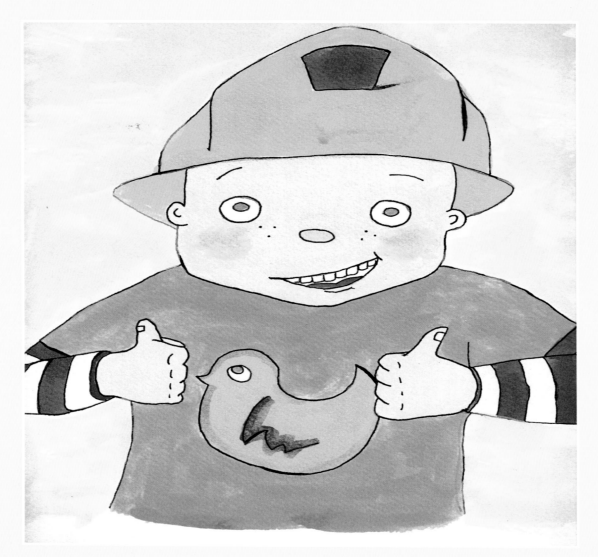

When he saw my new head, the fireman said that his special fireman's hat would fit me just right and it did! All the other boys and girls thought I was the luckiest boy in the hospital to have no hair on my head so that I could wear the big yellow hat.

When the fireman went home he let me keep the hat. And every day the children would come around to my bed to see it, which made me feel very lucky indeed!

On one of my visits to the hospital, I noticed that there were some hairs growing on the top of my head.

Doctor John said that because I had been a very brave boy and taken all my medicine I was getting better and my hair was starting to grow back.

Before I left the hospital, I met a girl called Lily. She was taking the same medicine as me and all of her hair was gone too.

She looked a little sad, so I told her that she could have my famous fireman's hat until her hair started to grow back just like mine.

She smiled a big smile when I gave her my famous hat and waved goodbye from the big hospital playroom. So what about you? Do you have a special story like mine? Why don't you tell me all about it on your Special Story Page?

Your Special Story Page

SPECIAL STORIES PUBLISHING

Kate Gaynor

Notes for Grown Ups on Childhood Cancer

Some of the most common types of childhood cancers are cancer of the kidney, malignant muscle tumours, lymphoma and leukaemia. The types of cancers that occur in children vary greatly from those seen in adults. They occur in different parts of the body and respond differently to treatment than adult cancers. The type of treatment a child receives depends on the type of cancer they have; however, a large percentage of children will receive chemotherapy treatment at some stage of their illness. Where cancer is concerned, chemotherapy is used to destroy the cancer cells or at least to control their growth. The most common approach to administering chemotherapy is by injection into the Hickman line, an injection into the muscles of the leg or by a continuous infusion into the Hickman line. Chemotherapy medicines can also be given in tablet or liquid form. Chemotherapy affects the bone marrow that produces the blood cells. Therefore fewer normal white cells are produced which means patients find it much more difficult to fight infection. Fewer red cells mean they are also easily fatigued and may often have anaemia. Fewer platelets also mean they tend to bruise and bleed more easily.

How to use this book

Treatment for childhood cancer can be very difficult to cope with, especially for very young children. A stay in hospital, having to contend with drips, tubes and injections is difficult enough without the possibility of hair loss for children to face. However, this book helps children to see the experience of a child that they can easily relate to. Harry not only enjoys his stay in hospital and makes new friends, but he also overcomes any fears of losing his hair. Most importantly, the book shows children that this experience is only temporary; it is not a permanent part of their lives. It assures them that there will be a time when their hair will start to grow back and they will leave the hospital and return home. The book also gives parents an opportunity to discuss the visit to hospital and the treatment with their child by comparing their experience to Harry's.

For further information in Ireland contact:

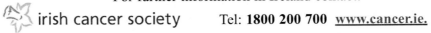 irish cancer society   Tel: **1800 200 700** www.cancer.ie.

For information outside of Ireland please contact your local cancer association.

Other books from Special Stories Publishing

A FAMILY FOR SAMMY: This story was written to help explain the process of foster care to young children.

JOE'S SPECIAL STORY: This story aims to help explain inter-country adoption to young children.

FIRST PLACE: The purpose of this book is to help children to understand and accept the effects of cleft palate, cleft lip or any speech impediment in their lives and most importantly, how best to overcome them.

THE WINNER: The intention of this book is to help explain Asthma and its effects to young children.

THE BRAVEST GIRL IN SCHOOL: The objective of this story is to help children with diabetes to appreciate the importance of taking their insulin injections and being aware of what they eat.

THE LOST PUPPY: This book has been designed to help children with limited mobility to see the positive aspects that using a wheelchair can bring to their lives.

To read more about the special stories collection, visit the Special Stories website at:
www.specialstories.net

Made in the USA
Middletown, DE
16 January 2016